# The Tale
# of a
# WOOD

*W1D*

# The Tale
## of a
# WOOD

Written and illustrated by

## HENRY B. KANE

## New York: Alfred A. Knopf

L.C. Catalog card number 62-7050

THIS IS A BORZOI BOOK,
PUBLISHED BY ALFRED A. KNOPF, INC.

For DAVID MARSHALL
woodsman of
the future

# CONTENTS

# I

# MORNING IN JULY

On a hot midsummer morning when the air was still and close and alive with the buzz of insects, the boy crossed the pasture on his way to the wood. He felt as though he was wrapped in an invisible blanket, stifling and oppressive. Then he reached the trees, and as he climbed over the barway he entered another world. The cool and damp of night still lingered under the towering pines, and their fragrance filled the air. Green leaves and thin grass gave life to the carpet of pine needles, and the boy sat down to drink in the refreshing sights and smells.

He had hardly settled himself against the trunk of a tree before the boy was discovered by a flock of chickadees. He heard the flip of their wings as they hopped through the branches overhead, peering down at him inquiringly and

1

asking over and over, "*chick-a-dee-dee-dee, chick-a-dee-dee-dee?*"

Canada mayflowers and partridge vines were all around him, their berries still bright green. Young pine cones littered the ground, some gnawed in half by squirrels. A ghostly white finger poked through the rust-colored needles, and he leaned closer to discover an Indian pipe, head bent under, pushing its way through to daylight. Then mosquitoes discovered him, and the boy rose to continue his way through the wood.

At the side of the path was a red-capped mushroom, its edges turned up like a saucer. One side had been chewed away, probably by a squirrel. The boy stooped to pick up a small feather, black with half-circles of white along its edges. He heard a gentle *tap-tap-tap* on a nearby tree. Maybe this feather had been dropped by that same woodpecker.

At the base of a high pine was a scattering of owl pellets. A horned owl's nest might have been hidden in that thick top. Many of the pellets had disintegrated and the bleached bones of mice and rabbits, disgorged by the night hunters and their young, were spread across the pine needles. As the boy pushed through the thick branches of low trees he was startled by a sudden rush underfoot, and looked ahead just in time to see the powder-puff tail of a rabbit disappearing from sight. He wondered who was the more surprised.

Where the pines become mixed with hardwoods there is an open glade, grass-covered for the most part, with a few clumps of sweet fern and a small stand of waist-high

poplars. The far side of the opening is carpeted with dark green moss and an occasional patch of gray reindeer moss, and tiny pines in their first and second year are sprinkled over it. This will not be an open space much longer.

The boy pulled aside the drooping branches of a hemlock to see the shinleafs he knew were hiding there. They were almost through blossoming. Only the top bells on their straight stems still held their petals. A half dozen mushrooms, the brown and white of lightly toasted marshmallows, floated on the sea of moss. One, which had not yet spread its cap, looked for all the world like a hen's egg nestled in a soft, green bed.

### ❧ Morning in July

A young crow, flying over the opening, swerved as he thought he saw a strange object under the low pines. His "car, car" immediately brought an older bird with a deeper voice to check on his discovery. They boy stood still, listening to the noisy consultation in the trees nearby, while more crows came over to see for themselves. Finally he stepped out from his half-cover, and with a loud clamor the noisy troop beat off hurriedly through the trees.

Along the edge of the brook where rock ferns drip from moss-covered boulders, the boy continued his way. Through the hemlocks, by the big sycamore, at last he came to the far side of the wood. As he neared the opening in the stone wall he was kept company by another flock of chickadees. They flitted through the branches ahead of and beside him, chattering incessantly to him and to one another. Someone else holds legal title to this wood, but it belongs, in fact, to the boy and the chickadees. He will visit it often in the future as he has so many times in the past, and they will be there to greet him and to bid him farewell.

# 2

# THE AGELESS WOOD

The warming sun of spring turns close-packed snow to crystal gems. The white cover grows thinner and thinner, melting away entirely around strong green plants that push out of their winter prison. These are club-mosses, and they have been doing this same thing for a very long time.

The place where the wood now stands was once a swamp —a hot, humid swamp. This was in the Coal Age, 300 million years ago, long before the Rocky Mountains and the Alps were thrust up. There were no trees as we know them, no grasses or flowers, but there were lush, dense forests of rank plants that reached 100 feet and more into the air. These were horsetails, ferns, and club-mosses, and all have survived to this day. The little plants that rise above the spring snow have stayed in existence in spite of stifling

heat and frigid blasts, of drought and flood and grinding
ice, but they have shrunk in size. They are towering trees
now only to the ants and beetles who crawl beneath their
spreading branches.

It was more than a billion and a half years ago that life
first appeared on earth. It was not an impressive appearance. This first life was so small and primitive that its
fossil remains can be seen only through a microscope. As
time went on tiny bacteria swarmed through warm waters
giving off iron oxide and sulphur compounds. They were
in such huge quantities over a long period of time that many
of today's great iron deposits were the result.

By 500 million years ago the evidence is clearer. The
scum that floated on still waters of those long-ago days
was made up of algae, tiny single-cell green plants with
chlorophyl, able to change air and water and sunlight into
starch. When another 200 million years had passed spore
plants had developed, the ferns, club-mosses, and horsetails
that made up the great forests of the Coal Age. Then, 200
million years ago, conifers appeared, pines and hemlocks
and all their kind with hard cones to protect their naked
seeds. Soon after came the enclosed seeds, giving rise to
the flowering trees and plants. Soon after? The flowering
trees, the hardwoods, came along about 150 million years
ago; the wild flowers something more than 50 million years
later. Geologically, these are not long times.

As the boy pushed through thick growth at the upper
end of the marsh on a summer's day, nothing was further
from his mind than the age of the plant kingdom. His
thoughts were of the redwings that scolded him, the bittern

that rose with a startled croak from his path and flapped heavily away, and the frogs lining the bank of the brook who leaped wildly into the water at his approach. He turned upstream to find a narrower crossing.

The shallow water of the sluggish stream had flowed into depressions on the muddy shore and come to rest in backwaters along its edge. In these stagnant pools was a rich growth of algae in colors of green, brown, and rust, the age-old, one-cell algae of long ago. On the still surface floated patches of iridescent blue scum that looked like oil. The boy kneeled down and touched one of the patches. It did not stick to his finger as oil would have done. Instead, it broke and pulled apart, leaving open water where the tip of his finger had been. It was a brittle, floating layer of iron oxide given off by microscopic bacteria in the water. The dawn-life of more than a billion and a half years ago was here before him, still producing iron as it has since the beginning.

A patch of horsetails grows along the brook, and when the boy crossed over he pushed through a rank growth of waist-high cinnamon ferns. He circled a huge boulder covered with green moss and masses of polypody, the rock fern, and as he entered the wood he walked across a broad area of ground pine and club-moss. These were the plants of 300 million years ago, the plants that were then trees, that toppled into their swamps to become today's coal.

As he walked across the springy floor of the wood, here deep in pine needles, the boy stooped to pick up a pine cone. It lay in a mat of ground pine which lifted its fruiting heads like tiny candelabra. He picked one of the heads

8

and looked at it closely. It seemed much like a small pine cone. He looked up at the thick green roof overhead and tried to imagine the ground pines and club-mosses looming over him, but somehow his imagination was not quite up to it. He could not place himself in a Coal Age jungle, but the pines under which he stood had an ancient lineage all their own. The boy had no trouble projecting himself back 200 million years into just such surroundings.

A path through the wood crosses an open glade, and here the pines and hemlocks are mixed with hardwoods.

Towering over the others is a giant sycamore, its bark a jigsaw puzzle of brown, green, and white. It is a tree with many holes which have provided homes for countless generations of squirrels, raccoons, and birds from chickadees to wood ducks. It was raising its zigzag branches high in the sky when the Pilgrims stepped ashore at Plymouth. It is also a tree with one of the oldest family histories of all our hardwoods, possibly the oldest. More than 100 million years ago when the sea still covered what is now the Rockies, ancestors of this sycamore grew in Greenland and around the Arctic Circle. They were the forerunners of the great hardwood forests of today.

In the shaded woods beyond the sycamore the boy stopped to admire a small stand of rattlesnake plantains. A dozen or so white flower spikes rose tall and slender above

white-veined leaves. These are orchids, the most recent family to develop in the plant world; yet even they were in existence long before man.

From the first skunk cabbages pushing up through ice and snow to the final flowering of the year when witch hazels burst into bloom, new life appears continuously; but it is not really new life at all. It is the repetition of a cycle of events that has been going on for a long, long time. While seas overflowed whole continents and then receded, while mountains thrust up into the clouds and then crumbled to flat plains, the plants grew and flourished. And here in this little patch of woodland is an outline of their entire history, from bacteria to orchids. Truly, this is an ageless wood.

# 3
# FAMILY AFFAIRS

On a morning in spring a barred owl perched in the thick cover of a big pine. He was close against the trunk of the tree, as inconspicuous as such a large bird could be, his eyes closed in sleep. A crow, flying close by, veered sharply and circled the treetop. His sharp eyes had seen a suspicious shape under the protecting branches, and he came around for a second look. That was enough. This was, indeed, a mortal enemy, and he sent out a clarion call for help.

In another part of the wood the boy heard the rising clamor. It grew louder and more raucous as crows came from far and near to join in the excitement. He could picture them swirling about the tree, landing on nearby branches to peer in at the cornered owl, all the while

13

screaming their hate. When the hubbub became even greater and then grew more distant, he knew that the discomforted bird had left his perch for another less conspicuous.

The chase was not yet over when the boy saw a black shadow slip silently into the top of a nearby pine. There could be only one reason why a crow would leave the fun of mobbing an owl. It must have family duties. Sure enough, as he neared the tree he saw the bird leave the far side as quietly as it had come, and high in the thick branches he could just make out a dark shape which must be a nest.

Climbing a full-grown pine is no easy task. In thick woods the lower limbs die as the tree reaches upward, so there is no foothold for the first fifteen or twenty feet. It was not a new problem for the boy. In an old carriage house at the edge of the wood was a long wooden ladder, patched in places and with an occasional board for a missing rung, but still strong and sturdy.

The ladder was heavy and awkward, as the boy knew well from past experience, but when he got it to the tree it reached into the first branches. These were dead and dangerous and he tested each one cautiously, his foot close to the trunk and with a firm handhold before he trusted his weight to it. On such a venture he knew he should have a companion in case of accident, but he continued his climb nonetheless. Soon he reached live branches, and by the time he got to the nest they were so thick he had difficulty squirming through them.

The nest was a bulky platform of sticks and twigs built on three branches close to the trunk. It seemed to be

crudely made, but it was strong and substantial. Inside, lying on a soft lining of grass and shredded bark, were five brown-spotted green eggs.

On a day in May a crack appeared in the shell of one of the eggs. It progressed slowly. Hours went by, but at last the shell fell apart to disclose a raw, naked baby crow. Thin eyelids were drawn tight over bulging eyes, and on the tip of its bill was the sharp white point with which it had cut its way to freedom. As its mother carried away the broken shell, the others were also hatching. At the end of the day five helpless birds huddled together in the bottom of the nest.

Although their scrawny necks seemed hardly strong enough to hold up their heads, whenever one of the parents appeared with food the newly hatched birds greeted it with open mouths held high. Caterpillars, beetles, and all manner of insects were stuffed into those gaping maws. After five days the young birds' eyes opened, blue-gray eyes which would later turn brown, and their raw, red skins were changing to gray. In less than two weeks body feathers began to appear, and by that time the fledglings had found their voices.

The boy heard the hoarse "car, car, car" when he was still far from the pine. The young crows were a month old now. He had visited them often, but this time, as he climbed nearer the nest, he saw that they were beginning to get restless. One stood on the rim and another was perched on a nearby branch. On previous visits he had handled them and they were completely unafraid. Now they shrank from

16

him and when he picked one up it suddenly flopped out of his hand and took off, followed by the others. The young birds were growing up. Their parents would continue to feed them for a while, but soon they would be on their own, adding their cracked voices to the early morning chorus, hunting across newly mowed meadows, and joining their kin in the boisterous badgering of owls.

The boy had been tempted to take a young crow for a pet, but he had had pet crows before and found them a mixed blessing. Taken from the nest when their flight feathers were just developing, they tamed readily and stayed nearby, even though they were completely free to leave at any time. They were alert, intelligent, and companionable —at times too companionable. The boy enjoyed blueberry picking in the lower pasture with a crow solemnly picking beside him. Together they ate almost as many as they picked. It was fun to see the amazement of friends when, at a whistle, a seemingly wild bird flew down out of the orchard to light on his shoulder. He found it difficult, however, to move silently through the wood with a noisy bird flying along overhead, lighting to peer at everything he stopped to examine, and if it was edible, gobble it down.

The boy's family objected to being wakened every morn-ing at daybreak by raucous calls from a bedroom window sill, and they never quite got used to the sudden swoop of a big bird snatching food from the table during the course of an outdoor meal. On washdays his mother soon became

Gt. Horned Owl
(Pine - several
years)

Coon
(Sycamore)

Fox
Den

Path

R.E.
Vireo
(Striped
Maple)

Flying
Squirrel
(Dead
Maple)

Grouse
(Foot of
small Pine)

tired of searching the orchard for clothes blown from the line because of stolen clothespins, and his father was even more upset when a heavy rain overflowed the roof gutters and the missing clothespins were discovered stuffed in the downspouts. It was always a relief when fall came and pet crows left to join the south-ward migration.

The crow's nest was big and bulky, about two feet across, yet it was so well placed in the thick pine top that it was difficult to see. Many other birds nested in the wood, and most of their nests were much smaller and even less conspicuous. Each year the boy kept score of the number of active nests he located. On a rough map of the wood he charted each one, and when autumn bared the trees he found, to his chagrin, many more that he had missed.

One spring the boy discovered a new hole high in an old oak. It seemed unnecessarily large for a flicker, and when days went by with no sight of its inhabitant, he sat down to wait. At last his patience was rewarded. Without warning, a big bird flashed over his head to sweep up into the oak. It landed on the trunk below the hole, looked alertly in all directions, then hitched upward. Its body was as big and black as a crow's. Its long, curved neck was black and white, topped by a head with a stout, gray bill and a startling bright red crest. Although he had never seen one before, the boy knew he was looking at a pileated woodpecker, a bird that once retreated before the advance of civilization but now, at last, was losing its fear of man

Crow
(Pine - 3rd
year)

19

Brook

Bluejay
(small Pine)

Towhee
(under small
bush)

Wood
Nest Chart

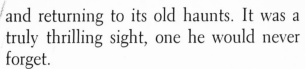

and returning to its old haunts. It was a truly thrilling sight, one he would never forget.

All summer and through the winter great holes appeared in dead stubs, made by the big woodpeckers as they dug deep for grubs. There were excavations in live trees as well, particularly hemlocks, sometimes a foot or more long and many inches deep. Axe-size chips showed the power of those strong bills. On occasion the wood rang to the woodpeckers' hammering, or to their loud "*cack-cack-cack*" call.

When another spring came the boy again took up his watch beneath the old oak, but this time no woodpecker came into view. Instead, at dusk, a pair of round, dark eyes stared from the nest hole. During the winter a barred owl had taken over and was not to be dispossessed.

The demand for tree holes is great. Large holes are appropriated by barred owls, wood ducks, and raccoons. Medium-sized holes are used by screech owls, sparrow hawks, crested flycatchers, and squirrels, and in spring there is always a waiting list for small holes. Chickadees, nuthatches, tree swallows, bluebirds, and wrens compete with flying squirrels and white-footed mice for old woodpecker holes. At this season the boy invariably carried a heavy stick for thumping on trees with holes. He was often surprised at what popped out.

Nests in tree holes are used year after year, if not always

by the same creatures. With a few exceptions, this is not true of exposed nests. By the time such a nest has gone through twelve months of wind, rain, sleet, and snow, it is usually in no condition to house another brood safely. Among the exceptions are the sturdy nests of crows and hawks, often strengthened and reused for years.

The boy knew well the nest of a red-tailed hawk. It was high in a mighty tree, one difficult to climb, but from the ground he could see the nest growing bigger and heavier each year. On one of his rare visits he found the two young were well-feathered and handsome birds. One drew back in the bottom of the nest, but the other stood on the rim and glared at him. He supposed this young bird was thoroughly frightened, but never in an adult hawk had he seen a fiercer or more untamed look. A red-tailed hawk is a bird to be admired.

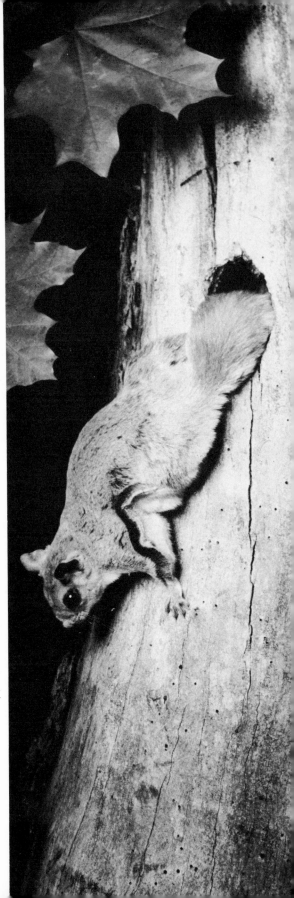

There are some nests which are well protected and seem to be in good condition, but which are not used a second year. A pair of phoebes nested in the old carriage house and swallows built on its rafters and under its eaves. They were evidently happy with the location, for each year they returned. Yet despite the fact that their old nests seemed in good shape, they immediately set about building new ones.

The boy's chart was not only a record of things past; it was also a guide to things to come. From the previous use of tree holes and the nests of crows and hawks, he had a good idea of where to look each spring. He felt certain, if winter had been kind to them, that the phoebes and barn swallows would be back in the carriage house. He also knew where to start looking for other nests. For three successive years orioles had hung their nests in the drooping branches of the same elm. There was every expectation that they would be back a fourth year.

Once a vireo built head-high in a striped maple beside the path. The boy was dismayed to think how many times he had walked by as it hung within reach, unseen. He did not discover it until autumn dropped the big green leaves that hid it from sight, but then it was entered on his chart.

Next year he would know where to begin the hunt for a hanging nest decorated with birch bark.

So it is with wood thrush and ovenbird, robin and blue jay, and most of the rest. If the birds survive the winter, chances are they will return to the same area and nest in the same general location as the year before. The boy's annual charts made interesting comparisons, although they had a certain sameness.

# 4
# THE OLD CARRIAGE HOUSE

At the edge of the wood stands a long-abandoned carriage house. In places brown shingles hang loosely from its sides, paint peels from its door and window frames, and wadded burlap replaces more than one broken pane. Under the protection of the eaves white-painted boards are evidence of a past elegance. From the front a grass-grown track, bordered by sugar maples, curves across an unkempt field past the tumbled foundations of what was once the big house, emerging onto a back road through stone gateposts.

The boy considers the carriage house his own, a refuge from sudden showers, an observation post looking out on field and wood, a hostelry which he shares with a variety of wild creatures. Bats roost in its cracks and crevices,

wasps hang paper homes from its board ceilings, mice find
it a shelter in winter, swallows and phoebes build on its
timbers and under its eaves.

A sliding door closes the wide entrance through which
proud horses once pulled shiny carriages. It keeps out
the snows of winter, but when spring bursts the maple buds
and the first birds return from the south, the door is left
hospitably ajar. It is not long before the phoebes enter. On
a beam over the door is a line of nests, the homes in which
many generations of young birds have been raised. Some
are bigger than others, for at times the phoebes have added
new stories on old homes.

Tragedy marked the phoebes' nest-building one year.
A few horsehairs still remain in the old box stall, favorite material for nest-building. One of the phoebes,

weaving a long hair into the nest, became entangled in
it. On his next visit the boy discovered the dead bird, hanging from its nest by a horsehair wrapped tightly around
its neck. That year there was no family, but the following
spring a pair arrived on schedule, probably the surviving
bird with a new mate.

For two years a pair of swallows built their jug-shaped
mud nests under the eaves. These were cliff swallows whose
ancestors nested on steep cliffs before white men arrived
and built barns. Their overhanging eaves were so attrac-
tive that now cliff swallows nest there by preference and
are often called eaves swallows as a consequence. During
the nesting season the boy rarely passed under the mud
home without squeaking. If anyone was inside a head immediately appeared at the round doorway. In the shadows

the white forehead patch stood out like a headlight, and a pair of beady eyes watched his every move.

Although the cliff swallows did not stay, there were always barn swallows, graceful birds with forked tails whose twittering flight is part of every country sky in summer. The sliding door was usually only slightly open, and the boy never ceased to be amazed at the narrow slit through which the barn swallows flew. A parent with a mouthful of insects would circle for an approach, then dive in a straight line through the opening without slackening speed. Sometimes the boy sat quietly beneath a nest to watch the feeding. A row of heads rested on the rim of the mud nest, close to the ceiling. They seldom moved. Except for their open eyes, the fledglings seemed asleep. But when a swift shadow appeared in the door opening all the heads came up at once, mouths open wide, like a row of jack-in-the-boxes. Even before her feet had touched the edge of the nest, the mother's bill was already inside one of those gaping mouths and a meal was being stuffed into it.

There are other flyers who return with the spring. Little brown bats, who have spent the winter hibernating in inland caves, return late when the insect supply is plentiful. All day they sleep in protected places, usually a thin crack behind a board or timber in a dry, man-made cave such as the carriage house. At dusk they hitch down into the

28

open, then fly out through the door opening to twist and dodge through the evening sky, scooping up mosquitoes and other insects, as much as half their weight in a night. Mother bats fly through the air with their one or two young clinging tight to their breasts. A young bat knows the feel of flight long before he himself can fly.

A board had pulled away slightly from the back of a beam. Beneath the narrow slit, a pile of droppings on the floor showed it to be a bat roost, and the boy investigated to see who was at home. At one end of the crack he pushed up a thin sliver of shingle and moved it along gently. Soon he could feel it come against something soft and yielding, and a high-pitched chittering told him he had found the first bat. It appeared quickly and launched itself into the room, soon to be joined by another and another, five in all. Back and forth they swirled, until at last three returned to their quarters. The other two settled in a corner under a beam, and the boy climbed on top of a barrel for a closer

look. One seemed trying to hide its head, but the other glared at him from tiny eyes, squeaking its anger in a thin, high voice. At last they, too, returned to continue their interrupted sleep.

The windows of the carriage house have many functions in addition to that of letting in light. Among others, they are effective insect traps. The sills are littered with the dead bodies of flies, wasps, and other insects who have blundered in at the door and tried to return outside through the unyielding glass. Spiders find them productive locations for their tangled webs. With the chill days of autumn many insects come inside, crawling into cracks and crannies to hibernate. When the warmth of spring wakes them from their winter's sleep many never get beyond the windows. Some of the paper-making wasps and mud-daubers, however, discover ways of getting outside and return to build nurseries for their young. Brown Polistes wasps hang paper cells from the ceiling. They rear their small families just as the white-faced hornets do, but without surrounding their single-layer cells with a paper cover.

Thread-waisted wasps plaster mud on the board walls to make homes for their young. Some are shapeless mounds with many cells. Others are carefully and beautifully made, several long tubes that look like pipe organs built side by side, each partitioned into a number of separate chambers. The mud-daubers who built them have stuffed each cell with paralyzed spiders, on one of which an egg has been laid. When the egg hatches, the grub will find a plentiful supply of fresh food. By the time it is gone the grub will have reached full size, and after going through the pupal stage will bite its way to freedom through the mud wall, emerging as a full-grown wasp.

Although the windows are washed only by the rains, they are clear enough to mirror the images of those outside. A robin discovered this. He had established a territory that

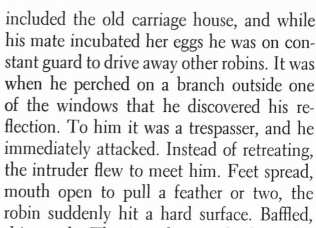

included the old carriage house, and while his mate incubated her eggs he was on constant guard to drive away other robins. It was when he perched on a branch outside one of the windows that he discovered his reflection. To him it was a trespasser, and he immediately attacked. Instead of retreating, the intruder flew to meet him. Feet spread, mouth open to pull a feather or two, the robin suddenly hit a hard surface. Baffled, he returned to his perch. The intruder was back on his perch. Time after time the irate bird repeated his attacks. He stopped occasionally to feed, but returned to take up where he had left off. He was back the next morning and the next and the next. By then the glass was streaked with mud from his feet, and at last he gave up. The boy, who had often watched the performance, never knew whether it was because the bird could no longer see himself, whether his young had left the nest so there was no further need to defend his territory, or whether it was because of complete frustration.

Raccoons are creatures of the night, but on a morning in late April one found herself far from home when dawn broke. Outside the carriage house a fallen limb lay against the brown shingle siding under a window. The raccoon climbed to the sill and looked inside. It was a dark cavern, a welcome cave. She scratched at the glass tentatively, then backed to the ground and set out to find an entrance. The fieldstone foundation was solid, but at last she came to the open door. For a moment she stood in the opening,

sniffing suspiciously, then squeezed inside and took up residence.

Although the boy stopped by often, it was more than three weeks before he discovered that the carriage house had a new tenant. On that morning he slipped quietly through the door opening, not wanting to disturb the phoebe if she was on the nest. Inside he paused to listen. Sometimes his silent approach was rewarded with the squeak of a startled mouse, the scampering of unseen feet, or the swish of wings. This time he heard a slight scratching and snuffling overhead. He went to the foot of the narrow stairway and started up. His head had almost reached the level of the upper floor when suddenly another head appeared. Black eyes peered into his from a black mask, hardly more than a foot away. For a startled moment the boy and the raccoon stared at one another. Then, with surprising speed, the coon whirled and raced across the board floor. By the time the boy's eyes had become adjusted to the semidarkness of the loft, she had disappeared.

There are few hiding places in the loft. A closet, a wall cupboard, a few stacked boxes, and an old trunk are about all. There are spaces under the eaves, but the openings are so narrow that it hardly seemed possible for anything as large as a coon to squeeze through. Nevertheless, the boy peered into each in succession, his face pressed against the sloping roof boards. His flashlight revealed tangled spider webs, debris of old mouse and squirrel nests, piles of nut shells and seed husks, and at last the shining eyes of the raccoon. Her brown, furry body seemed to fill the cramped space to overflowing, and she stared fearlessly at the boy. Then there was a movement under her chin, and another black mask appeared, a much smaller mask with two inquiring eyes peering from it. The boy gasped in amazement, and then a second round face pushed out from under its mother's thick fur. Where there had been one raccoon a few weeks before, now there was a family.

The boy was never certain how many baby coons he had seen. Little faces constantly appeared and disappeared, but he thought there must be four, possibly five. He had no opportunity to check his count, for that night the mother moved her children to other, and hopefully less cramped, quarters.

Another animal that strayed into the carriage house found it more difficult to leave. Probably the skunk had entered to hunt mice, not to seek shelter, but in any event it found itself trapped in an empty grain bin. A pile of boards outside made it easy to climb to the rim, and the open cover was an invitation to tumble in. Once inside, however, there was no way out except to climb straight walls, and unlike the raccoon, the skunk was no climber.

The boy had not visited the old building for several days, so he had no way of knowing how long the skunk had been in its prison. However, from the aimless way it shuffled back and forth, back and forth, it seemed to have given up all hope of escape. It would need help. A board slid over the edge as a ladder would be too steep for it to climb. There seemed only one answer: the skunk would have to be lifted out.

The boy had never before caught

a full-grown skunk, but he had seen his father do it. He had been told that the scent sacs at the base of the animal's tail were closed off by a bone when the tail was down, but when it was raised the sacs were open and ready to shoot a spray of penetrating musk to the rear. He hoped he had been told correctly.

Slowly the rescuer leaned over the waist-high front of the bin and reached down. The captive stopped his pacing and started to raise his tail. The boy froze. When the skunk dropped his tail and again began pacing, the boy reached still lower. There were several such stops and starts. As long as that tail was down, the boy knew he was safe. Slowly, very slowly, he reached out.

The skunk's head was in a far corner of the bin and he rocked from side to side on his front feet. The boy's hand reached for the black and white tail, nearer, nearer, nearer. Suddenly he lunged, grabbing the bushy tail and lifting at the same time. As the surprised animal's hind feet came off the floor his tail and backbone were in a straight line. The musk sacs were closed. The boy stood up, holding his prize at arm's length. Four black feet clawed vainly at thin air. There was a slight nauseous odor, but the snatch had been too quick for any real discharge. The boy carried his catch outside. Going around to the stone wall, he reached across and dropped the confused animal on the far side. There was no resentment at the rough handling, no angry departing spray. Instead, as the boy peered cautiously over the wall, the liberated skunk waddled off through the trees. He was in no great hurry. He seemed as certain of immunity to attack as his tribe has always been. Even his late unsettling experience did not seem to have shaken his self-confidence.

36

Few wild creatures live together in peace and harmony. The varied inhabitants of the old carriage house and the occasional visitors who wander in are not seeking company. They come for reasons of their own, and most of them either tolerate or ignore one another. It has attractions for so many, however, that it is a natural gathering place, the community center of the wood.

# 5
# DANCE OF THE PROMETHEAS

Long before the sun had set, the lengthening shadows of the wood crept out across the pasture. From somewhere in the gathering gloom a hermit thrush poured out his clear, flute-like song. By the time the sun's last rays had painted the tops of the tallest trees with gold, the floor of the wood was in darkness. Leaves rustled as the first mouse scampered from hiding. An owl called mournfully. Night falls swiftly in the wood.

At the edge of the trees where the stone wall marks the pasture bound, it was not yet dark. The crimson sky had faded to a greenish-blue and the evening star shone brightly in the west. A big moth fluttered along the tree line. Another joined it, then another and another, until the darkening sky seemed filled with aimless flyers. They

39

dipped under low branches, swept across the pasture grass, and swirled high over the treetops. It was the spring dance of the Prometheas, the male moths in search of a mate. They were answering the age-old call of a female, waiting somewhere close by.

Wild cherry trees grow along the wall and straggle out into the pasture. None are very large—some no more than switches. Dried leaves hang from a few all winter, but they are no ordinary leaves. Each is tied securely to the twig with silken threads, and it is rolled up to hide the cocoon of a Promethea moth.

In spring the cherry trees burst into bloom, beautiful white clouds along the edge of the wood. When the leaves unfurl, life stirs inside the cocoons. They are well and firmly built, hard and strong except in one place. At the top their silken walls are drawn together loosely like the puckered top of a paper bag.

On a May morning as the boy walked along beside the wall, he saw a slight movement in one of the cherry trees. He peered beneath its leaves and there, hanging from a twig, a Promethea cocoon swayed and jerked. The boy knew what was about to happen, and he sat in the grass beside it to watch. Soon the top of the cocoon spread open, made soft by a liquid its occupant had ejected, and a furry head pushed through. Big, feathery antennae showed this to be a male. The moth wasted no time

40

and was soon free of his winter home.

The Promethea's long body looked much like a furry caterpillar, and his crumpled wings hung down like a wad of soft flannel. Now that he was free the moth backed down the dead leaf until he reached its tip. There he hung while the wings slowly unfurled, pulled down by gravity as strength flowed into them. When at last they had reached full size, the moth's body had shrunk to normal. He lifted one fur-covered leg after another. He rubbed them over his fern-like antennae. For an hour or more he hung there, lazily opening and closing his dark wings and feeling their new stiffness. The boy had given up watching long before the big moth made his first flight. By then it was midafternoon. At dusk he was ready to take his place in the dance of the Prometheas.

Nearby, just above the cocoon from which she had recently emerged, a female hung patiently from a twig. She was more brightly colored than the dark male and had smaller antennae. Her body was big and heavy with eggs.

Now she sent out her call, an odor which the boy could not have sensed but which was irresistible to male Prometheas. It was so far-reaching that they answered from across the pasture, from the other side of the wood, from far places a mile or more downwind. They came by scores to join in the dance, to seek out the place where she waited. At last one found her and fluttered down on the twig

**41**

by her side. The hunt was over.

The life of a Promethea is short. After mating, the female flew heavily at night through the low growth, laying her eggs on cherry, sassafras, spicebush, and other leaves, a few here and a few there. Each egg was fastened tight with sticky, reddish glue. In a few days her fat, swollen body was greatly shrunken. None of these giant moths have mouth parts, so when they use up the energy they bring from the cocoon there is no way to replenish it. Having done their part to perpetuate their kind, they are exhausted. Their battered wings no longer have the strength to carry them, and they drop to the floor of the wood to die.

The warmth of the sun reached inside the round eggs, and in a dozen days they are ready to hatch. An opening appeared in one. It grew larger and then a small black head appeared, followed by a yellow and black body, as the first caterpillar wriggled out onto the leaf. A second gnawed his way free of another egg, then another and another until all eight had emerged. They wasted no time. Pausing only long enough to eat the shells of their empty eggs, they crawled to the edge of the leaf and there, in a row, began to eat. There was no danger they would exhaust their food supply, for the female had distributed her eggs widely. These eight caterpillars had an entire tree to them-

42

selves, their private larder.

The caterpillars grew fast, and soon their skins became tight and uncomfortable. They stopped eating, and for a day or so clung motionless under protecting leaves. Four days after hatching they were ready to shed their skins. The skin split at the back of each one's head and the silkworm wriggled it down over its body as though squirming out of an old sweater. The discarded skin still clung to the leaf and the caterpillar turned to eat it hungrily. The new color was a beautiful clear yellow, but soon black rings began to reappear and the earlier markings returned.

Four times the caterpillars changed their coats, and at last they were full-grown. Now they looked nothing like the tiny creatures that emerged from the eggs. They were more than two inches long, with smooth bluish-green skins. Rows of shiny black dots in blue circles decorated them like buttons. Just behind its head each had four bright red knobs, and a yellow one stuck up from one of its rear segments. The Prometheas are very colorful caterpillars.

It was not entirely by chance that the boy saw one of the silkworms spinning its cocoon. He had discovered them some time before and had kept a close watch ever since. It was six weeks after hatching that the first one stopped eating forever. For hours it rested, then set to work fashioning a cocoon in which, unseen, it would change into a

moth. And it was just at that moment that the boy came by on a regular inspection.

Prometheas belong to the family of Saturniids, or Giant Silkworm Moths, a family which includes the Cecropias, as big as a man's hand, and the ghostly Lunas with long, trailing wings. Except for the Prometheas they are all creatures of the night, often mistaken for bats as they fly across a moonlit sky. The caterpillars of the Saturniids have one thing in common—they are all spinners of silk, as pure and strong as the silk of commerce.

As the boy watched, the caterpillar left the leaf on which it had rested and moved to another. It examined the surface carefully and then a thin, shiny thread came from its mouth. Gluing it to the leaf, the caterpillar swung its head across to the edge and stuck the thread down there as well. Back and forth, back and forth, went the silkworm's head, and in short order the entire surface was covered with a filmy coat of gleaming white silk.

The Promethea knew nothing about changing seasons. It had no knowledge that the cherry leaves would loose their hold with the first frosts and fly off in the winds of autumn, but instinct made the silkworm act as though it did. It moved up onto the leaf stem and wrapped it around and around with silk. It climbed to the twig above and threw countless strands around that too, tying the leaf so fast that even the strongest blasts of winter would not tear it loose.

The caterpillar then began to thicken the silken layer on the leaf, shortening the threads as it did so. Slowly the edges of the leaf began to curl in until at last they

44

were pulled together. Then the spinner began to shape an oval shell inside. It turned about constantly, up and down, and as the wall thickened the fat body pressed it into a hard, tough chamber. At no time was the brilliant silken strand broken. It was one continuous thread, and by the time the Promethea had finished it was several hundred feet long. Countless generations of Saturniid caterpillars had spun their winter homes in the same way before.

The boy did not watch the complete home-building. It took many hours, well into the night. Even if he had stayed he could not have seen the final touch as the caterpillar coated the inside with a fluid which dried to make its home as hard and firm as a nut.

The finished cocoon was much smaller than the caterpillar had been when it started, but so much liquid had been used in the building that its green body had shrunk to less than half its original size. Safe from prying eyes, it now went through another great transformation. Sev-

eral days went by, then the shrunken caterpillar once more shed its skin. This time, as the old skin was wriggled down into a shapeless wad, a shiny brown object appeared inside the cocoon. It was a pupa, third stage in the life cycle of all moths, butterflies, and many other insects.

When winter winds whistle through bare branches and

snow lies deep over the stone wall and through the wood, a few dry leaves still cling to wild cherry twigs. They whip back and forth in the blast and freezing rains coat them with ice, but they hold fast. Inside, safe in their own private worlds, the pupae wait for the call of spring. Some will push forth to wait patiently for an answer to their long-distance messages; and some will take to the air to join in one of the wood's most ancient rites, the mating dance of the Prometheas.

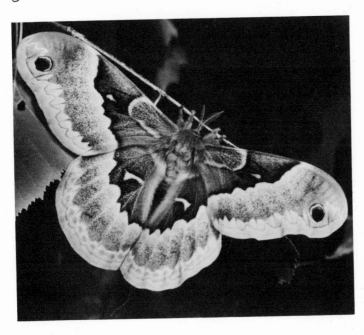

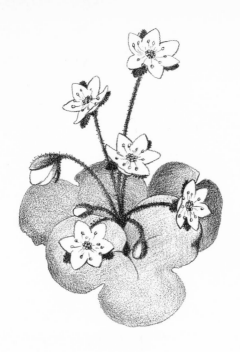

# 6

# GARDEN OF THE WOOD

In open places the changing seasons bring changing colors. The meadow becomes a field of gold or white, as mustard, buttercups, goldenrod, and daisies come into bloom. The surface of the pond is white on a July morning as water lilies open their petals to the rising sun. The wet marsh is a sea of purple in midsummer when the rank stands of Joe-Pye-weed burst into flower. There are no such color changes on the floor of the wood.

In the filtered sunlight under the trees most plants grow alone or in small patches. Colorful as they are, violets, fringed polygalas, lady's-slippers, and columbines do little

49

to affect the overall pattern of green and brown. Even where close-packed Canada mayflowers blanket the ground, their foamy white flowers are almost lost in the green cover. The garden of the wood is seen only by those who take the trouble to hunt it out. It is a rewarding hunt.

The boy knows the garden well, the rocky slopes where columbine nod in spring, the mossy bank studded with tiny white violets like stars in a sky of green, and the shady places where ghostly Indian pipes push through the thick pine needles of mid-summer. He knows where to search for the elusive whorled pogonias and bottle gentians, and the place where a climbing fern straggles through the lower branches of a blueberry bush is his secret alone.

Plants and flowers mean many things to many people. To a botanist they are material to be collected, dissected, catalogued, and studied. To a photographer, the preservation of their passing beauty on film is a constant challenge. To an artist or a poet they are incentive and inspiration. The boy was none of these. He loved them as they were and where they were for their beauty and, in some cases, for their fragrance. One of the great delights of spring was to bury his face in a clump of pink arbutus.

He also discovered early in life that such fragile and elusive flowers as those of the wood should be left as they are, not picked for a household bouquet. Most are too sensitive to last out the journey but, more importantly, many cannot be picked without disturbing their roots and killing the plants. Once-common wild flowers soon become rare as city dwellers move to the country and thoughtlessly

strip the woodlands. Such rank flowers of the fields and roadsides as daisies, goldenrod, and tansy can take care of themselves. No amount of picking can discourage them.

It was mayflowers, the trailing arbutus, that first opened the boy's eyes to a side of nature he had not known. He had learned the names of most plants from someone else, but they were not always correct. Still others he had identified from a small book with scanty and incomplete information. Then he discovered a thorough and accurate guide. From this book he found that every plant belongs to a family, and that close relatives do not always resemble one another. It was no surprise to learn that rhododendrons and mountain laurel are members of the same family. They look alike. But it was certainly a surprise to find that arbutus and blueberries are also related to them. It was the start of a new and absorbing interest.

The entire history of plant life, starting with the algae in the brook, is here in the wood, and the latest and most varied of all plants are the wild flowers. As new forms develop older ones do not disappear. They continue to grow side by side, just as ferns and club-mosses and pines do. The wood is a living history of wild flowers, written in a beautiful language. Those who stop to read find it a fascinating story.

Flowering plants came into being about 150 million years ago with the appearance of hardwood trees. Another 50 million years or more went by before the first flowering plants without woody stems developed, the wild flowers. It took that long for the first small flower-producing plant to appear, the forerunner of all today's flowers. Descendants

of that ancient plant still flourish. They are in the meadow and along the stone wall at the edge of the wood. They grow tall and rank in damp places by the brook. That dawn-plant, the world's oldest wild flower, was the original buttercup, although it certainly looked very little as it does today when it first came into being.

As a small child buttercups had meant only one thing to the boy, a means of determining a friend's like or dislike of butter. If the shiny petals reflected yellow under his chin, it was the occasion for setting up a chant, "Johnnie loves butter, Johnnie loves butter." When he outgrew that stage, buttercups lost their interest. They were so commonplace they were completely ignored in the search for other and more exotic flowers. Then he learned of their age-old lineage.

Looking out the door of the carriage house, the boy saw a waving green field dotted with daisies and the brilliant orange of devil's paint-brush. Here and there were occasional clumps of yarrow, and the patch of blue was vetch climbing through the tall grass. And everywhere, the yellow eyes of buttercups. He wondered how the field would have looked when those buttercups' ancestors were the only flowers. It would not have been a field of grass, for one thing. Grass, too, is a flowering plant, and it arrived long after the first primitive buttercups.

Flowers did not develop for the purpose of beautifying the landscape, although they do that exceedingly well. It would be a drab world without them. They exist for the sole purpose of producing seeds, and two flower-parts are almost always needed. Pistils are the parts that hold the eggs. Stamens produce pollen, and when the pollen is carried from stamen to pistil the flower is fertilized and the eggs develop into seeds. Two other parts of most flowers are petals and sepals. Sepals form the cover of a flower bud which opens to let the petals expand, and the petals especially are a lure for insects.

The boy picked a buttercup and looked at it closely. It was complete with all four parts clearly separated, typical of primitive flowers. Some of those that developed later have only pistils, others only stamens. Some, such as marsh marigolds which look like buttercups and are members of the same family, have eliminated petals entirely. Their yellow sepals look like petals. There are flowers in which the same kind of parts have completely different appearances. A lady's-slipper has three petals. Two are narrow wings that stand out at the sides; the third is the inflated pink sac that brightens the wood in June.

In the buttercup's center the pistils are bunched together in a shape that reminded the boy of a pine cone, spiralling up to a rounded top. It is evidence of a direct line of descent from the cone-bearing plants, a shape that is common to the centers of many later and more complex flowers such as black-eyed Susans. Stamens curve up from under the base of the cone, a large number of them. Then come five shiny yellow petals, the color of farm butter and shaped like a cup. And finally, under the petals, the green sepals, five of them also. This is a complete flower, and it has looked like this for millions of years. While its descendants have grown more and more complex, pampered in greenhouses, beribboned at flower shows,

55

PETALS

SEPALS

STAMENS

PISTIL

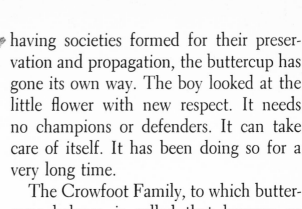

having societies formed for their preservation and propagation, the buttercup has gone its own way. The boy looked at the little flower with new respect. It needs no champions or defenders. It can take care of itself. It has been doing so for a very long time.

The Crowfoot Family, to which buttercups belong, is called that because so many of its members have deeply cut leaves that look something like a crow's foot. Some of the flowers of this family have the same appearance as buttercups. In the wood there are hepaticas, wood anemones, and marsh marigolds, among others. Then there are columbines, whose beautiful nodding heads seem to have nothing in common with the flowers of near relatives.

The Rose Family is almost as primitive as the Crowfoot. Its flowers, too, are separate and complete, but this is a family whose members are trees and shrubs as well as small plants. Apples, pears, and most other orchard trees are members of the Rose Family. So are raspberries, blackberries, and strawberries, and the blossoms of all of them look very much alike. The tiny yellow-flowered cinquefoil growing along paths through the wood and the tall meadowsweet of wet places are also relatives. And from the fragrant, pink wild roses that give the family its name, have come the glamorous cultivated roses of formal gardens and estates.

So it goes with the rise of succeeding families, most of them named for their most familiar if not their first

56

members. There are the Mustard, Pea, Carrot, and Heath Families, and the Figworts or Snapdragons. Then come the more advanced plants such as the mints, composites, and grasses, the latter two the most widespread and numerous of all, and probably the latest to develop, the Orchid Family.

Lying on his stomach on a bed of pine needles, the boy studied the nodding heads of a pair of lady's-slippers, one of the wood's several orchids. Now that he knew something of the structure of flowers, he wondered how it was possible for a flower that hid its essential parts so completely to be pollinated. He heard the drone of a bee, and looked about to see a bumblebee approaching. She had just left a nearby lady's-slipper and now headed for the one directly in front of the boy.

Down the top of the pink sac was a long slit. It was here the bee landed and immediately began to push her way inside. The slit spread open, and as the bee entered it closed behind her like a spring door. The boy could not see the bee sipping the nectar inside, nor could he see her confusion when she discovered the entrance door closed. But he could see the flower dip and sway as the angry insect buzzed about. The buzzing ended when she discovered the exit hole at the top of the sac and crawled up

to it, and as she did pollen from the previous flower was brushed off her back. Then, as she squeezed under this flower's pollen box, a new dusting replaced that which she had left behind. When the boy saw her push

through the top door her back was as covered with pollen as when she entered.

Most flowers must be fertilized by pollen from other flowers, not their own. Lady's-slippers have found an ingenious way of making certain this happens.

The boy was no library naturalist, but an explorer of the outdoors. However, having discovered something new to him, he needed books to tell him what he had found. They also opened his eyes to what he should look for in the future. He had learned of the relationship of plants in families; now he found that there are further groupings inside families.

First of all there is a "species" composed of plants so much alike there is seemingly no difference. All pink lady's-slippers are the same species; all white pines are another species. There are more than 250,000 different species in the world. Then there is a "genus" which is made up of species having more things in common with one another than they do with other plants. All species of lady's-slippers are members of the same genus; all pines belong to another genus. And finally there is the "family," a grouping of genera (the plural of genus), which have certain things in common such as the number of petals, stamens, or other basic characteristics.

It was when the boy had learned this much that he came to understand the reason for the unpronounceable Latin names used by botanists. More than 200 years ago Linnaeus, the great Swedish botanist, devised a system of naming plants to overcome the great confusion which comes from using popular names. There are often several different common names for the same plant. What one person calls a pink lady's-slipper another calls a stemless lady's-slipper or a moccasin-flower. Linnaeus gave a very descriptive name to the genus of lady's-slippers, Cypripedium. In Latin it means "slipper of Venus." Then he gave each species a name, that of the pink lady's-slipper being acaule, meaning stemless. Its full name is a combination of the two, Cypripedium acaule. The name of the genus always comes first. The species name may be the latinized version of the place where a plant grows or where it was first found, such as "virginiana"; or it may come from its discoverer, as "hookeri" refers to Mr. Hooker. There are various other sources but one combination of names belongs to only one plant, and it is understood and used by botanists all over the world. This is one language they all speak.

The boy did not believe he would ever find it necessary to call the buttercups along the brook "Ranunculus septentrionalis," but it was useful to know how to identify them definitely. Further, his introduction to this method of naming plants gave him understanding of the same system of classifying all living things—birds, animals, reptiles, and the rest. It was especially useful with insects, many of which have no common names. The wasps who hang their open paper nests in the old carriage house have no such popular names as yellow-jackets or mud-daubers. They are known only by the Greek name of their genus, Polistes.

Everything in the wood has something of interest for the boy, its birds and animals, insects and reptiles, its towering pines and its spreading oaks. Not the least are its plants and flowers. He had always loved them for themselves, but his new-found understanding of their history, family relations, and unique adaptations gave him an entirely different kind of appreciation. The lowly buttercup, too common to be noticed before, had achieved new status. The involved way in which many flowers have developed gave them new fascination. The garden of the wood is a place in which a boy, or a girl, could spend a lifetime without learning all it has to teach.

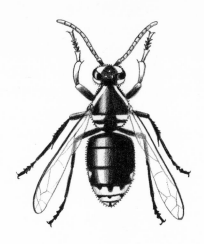

# 7

# GRAY PAPER HOME

An old rotted log provides good insulation from the freezing cold of winter, but it warms through slowly. Flowers carpet the wood before the soft breath of spring melts its icy shell and releases the sleepers inside. One by one the sow bugs, millipedes, and beetles make their way out. Almost the last to leave is the white-faced hornet queen.

For a short time the queen flies from flower to flower, sipping the sweet nectar and strengthening her wings. Then, ready to begin her family duties, she starts a paper home.

It was on a morning in May that the boy first saw the white-faced queen. She was stripping the weathered gray surface from a rail fence at the edge of the wood. Slowly the boy edged closer until he was no more than a yard

63

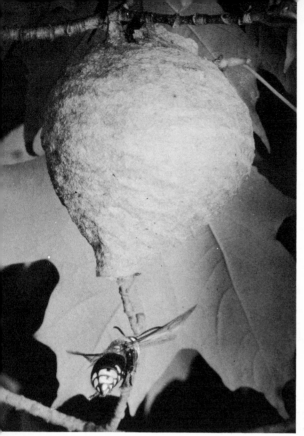

away. The hornet took no notice as she backed along the rail, gouging out a thin strip of wood fibers and chewing them into a ball. Then, having all she could carry, the queen took off along the edge of the wood.

Although she soon disappeared from sight, the boy knew the hornet was building somewhere nearby. He followed the direction of her flight until, looking back, he could just see the rail where she had been working, then waited. In a few minutes he heard a loud buzz and saw the queen return to the same spot. He watched as she rolled up another ball, and when she left it was to fly directly over his head into the lower branches of a sugar maple no more than a dozen feet away.

It took some time to find the nest. The spreading branches of the maple offered a thousand hiding places, but at last the boy discovered it. The little gray nest looked like a paper bag hung upside down. The queen had fixed it firmly to a twig, and now she was adding to its funnel-like opening. When she left for more building material, the boy looked up through the narrow entrance. Dimly he saw the layer of brood cells inside. Not until the frosts

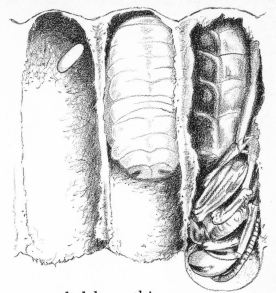

came would he again dare to come so close to that doorway.

The hornet queen starts her nest with only a few cells placed side by side, a thick pancake hung from a twig. The cells are open at the bottom, and at the top of each she glues an egg. By the time those eggs hatch into white grubs the comb is surrounded by a thin cover of paper, real paper, made by chewing wood pulp with the queen's sticky saliva. Men may well have learned the secret of papermaking from the wasps and hornets.

The queen is even busier when her eggs begin to hatch. Now she must feed the grubs. Their diet is varied, usually the half-chewed remains of insects, but sometimes the nectar of flowers or the juice of ripe fruits. The grubs grow fast and in two weeks or less are ready for the next stage of their existence. They spin silken cocoons inside their cells with rounded domes over the mouths, and in privacy change into pupae. The shapeless grubs now have the form of adults with legs and antennae folded close against their soft bodies and tiny wings pressed against their sides. In little more than a week they are ready to emerge.

When the first of her brood cut open the silken caps of their cells and crawl out into their gray home, the queen's housekeeping duties are almost done. At first her children are weak and wobbly, but as she feeds them their bodies

65

harden and their wings grow strong enough for flight. Then they take over the running of the nest. From that day on the queen spends all her time laying eggs while the workers wait on her, run the nursery, and enlarge their home.

The boy came often to the nest. From a safe distance he watched the increasing stream of insects fly in and out of its door. Through his glasses he saw them arrive with half-chewed caterpillars and other insects, or balls of wood pulp to add to their expanding walls. He saw house-cleaners leave with dead grubs, caterpillar remains, and other debris. He saw other workers emerge with chewed paper stripped from the interior to add to the outside shell. He knew that the inside was being enlarged, that the little gray nest which started with only a dozen or so cells would have a hundred times that many before the season was over.

On a hot day in midsummer the hornet's nest is a busy place. It has grown as large as a man's head and more than two thousand white-faced insects make it their home. The bulging silk cap on a cell splits open as a young hornet pushes her way out. She steps slowly across the bottom of the comb to its edge, then climbs up over the rim to rest. She cleans her front legs and antennae, pulling them through her black-rimmed jaws. A worker hurries by with food for the grubs. The newcomer reaches out an antenna and the worker answers the signal by giving the young

hornet her first meal as an adult. She is still pale and weak, so for a day or two she stays in the nest, gathering strength to take her place as a working member of the community.

During her first few weeks the new worker is a hunter and builder. She hawks through the grass and trees, pouncing on caterpillars and other insects whose chewed remains provide a soft pap for the hungry grubs. She makes countless trips to the weathered fence, bringing back balls of pulp to add to her growing home. At last she loses her youthful energy and is content to spend the rest of her days as a housekeeper, cleaning out old cells to make way for new occupants, feeding grubs with food brought by the hunters, and disposing of debris. At times she herself eats insects, but she prefers nectar and fruit juices.

The compound eyes of hornets, like those of flies, dragonflies, and many other insects, are made up of hundreds of separate lenses. Facing in all directions, these lenses give a wide range of vision, but an insect may not be able to interpret the picture it sees clearly. One day as the boy stood beneath the eaves of the carriage shed, he saw a hunting white-face. She flew in and out between the rafter ends searching for likely prey. Suddenly she pounced on a round black object. It was a nailhead, but she had to feel it with her antennae before discovering her mistake. A luckless green caterpillar soon made up for the error.

68

As the days grow shorter and the nights chillier, the workers make ready for another year, a year they will not see. They build larger cells around the edge of the lower comb and add another smaller comb. The queen lays her last eggs but this time, when the young emerge, they are not workers but princesses and males. When they leave the nest to mate, the end of the colony is near. In the few warm days that are left, the workers continue their duties, but with the first frosts they die by the hundreds. Grubs are left untended or are pulled from their cells to die outside. Some of the pupae push through their silken cell caps to emerge on warm days, but after wandering listlessly about the deserted nest they, too, die.

The new princesses, however, have a happier fate. After a few carefree days they seek out sheltered places in which to spend the winter. Some hide under bark, some crawl into cracks and crevices in stone walls and old fences, some burrow into the soft punk of rotted logs. Not all will live through the freezing cold of winter, but when spring comes again a few will leave their shelters to begin anew the cycle of the gray paper home.

# 8

# MOON OF THE YOUNG

All day and well into the night, soft, wet snow fell from leaden skies. Before dawn the clouds rolled back from a star-studded sky, and the morning sun burst on a world of white that danced and sparkled in the early light. Every bough and twig wore a heavy coat, and gray birches along the stone wall bent double, burying their heads in the thick, white blanket.

In the wood few tracks broke the surface of the snow. Most of the cottontails were still hidden in their comfortable burrows. Partridge and pheasant had not yet burst from their hiding places under snow-buried boughs. But along the stone wall and around white mounds which hid clumps of juniper, a maze of tracks told of the white-footed mice who had played under the stars. They looked like small cottontail or squirrel tracks, the marks of the

hind feet ahead of those of the front, often followed by a straight line where a long tail had flicked the snow.

The snow was a robin-storm of April. Before noon the warm sun had stripped the twigs of their thick coverings, dropping them into the soft white surface below. It was pitted with holes like craters of the moon. They wiped out a white-foot trail that led to the stone wall and vanished down a hole. Melting snow sent trickles of water down the hole, but it was soaked up by the thirsty earth long before it reached the soft nest where four raw, new baby mice nestled in the warmth of their mother's fur.

As the days went by the young mice grew fast. Within a week they were covered with a coat of short fur, gray above and white below; in two weeks their eyes were open; and by the end of the third week they had been weaned and were eating seeds brought by their mother.

A month after the April snow the young white-footed mice came to the mouth of their tunnel for the first time. They huddled together in this strange above-ground world, drinking in the night smells of spring, noses twitching and long whiskers quivering. Their round, black eyes, especially acute in the dim threshold light cast by the stars, saw every moving leaf and crawling insect around them, and their big ears took in the slightest sound. The startling call of a hooting owl sent them tumbling back down the tunnel, but two nights later the young mice left their home forever.

It had taken less than five weeks from the time they were born for the white-footed mice to be on their own. It takes little if any longer for young shrews, moles, and meadow mice to leave their nests. But most larger animals stay in their mother's care for longer periods while she teaches them caution and the ways of making a living. During spring and early summer the wood has its full share of them.

As the boy walked along the path under the big pines, he saw a sudden flash of color in the open glade ahead. Cautiously he moved toward it, keeping well hidden behind tree trunks and low growth, until he could see out into the open space. There, something he would never have thought possible—a rabbit was chasing a blue jay!

In all the woods there are few creatures more timid than

cottontail rabbits. They are
hunted by owls, hawks, foxes,
and other predators, and since
they are completely defenseless they continue to exist only
by running away. At this they
are expert. It was a rare and
puzzling sight, therefore, to
see one take the offensive. The
blue jay did not seem overly
concerned. When the boy got
a clear view of what was happening, the bird was standing
alertly on the ground, crest raised, head cocked on one
side. Then the rabbit made a lunge and the jay flew up,
landing again a dozen feet or so away. Several times this
was repeated. It seemed more like a game than anything
else, but at last the bird tired of it and took off screaming
through the trees, leaving the field of battle to the victorious
rabbit.

It was only when the cottontail hopped slowly to a
patch of Canada mayflowers that the boy suspected the
reason for the amazing scene he had witnessed. When he
left his hiding place the rabbit hurriedly disappeared. She
had had enough combat for one day. Carefully, watching
every step, the boy approached the green sea of leaves.
It took some time, but at last he found what he was after,
a ball of grass and hair sunk in a hole hardly larger than
his two fists. Cautiously he parted the soft mass and there,
hidden inside, were four baby rabbits, their eyes not yet
open. The mother instinct to protect her young is strong

even in defenseless creatures.

A few days later the nest was empty, but a short distance away the boy came on a tiny rabbit crouched at the base of a pine. It showed no fear but looked at him wide-eyed as he came nearer and nearer. Slowly he reached out a hand, a green leaf in his fingers, but even at that age the cottontail had a natural sense of distrust. It raised its head slightly, nose wiggling, then suddenly turned and scampered off through the trees. The boy knew it would not always be as fortunate in its meetings with strangers. The life of a rabbit is short.

Many years ago a limb had fallen from high in the big sycamore. Now a hole in the trunk marked the place where it had broken off, a hole which had been home to a variety of birds and animals. Several times the boy had seen raccoon tracks nearby and he suspected there might be a family inside, but he was not certain until the day he surprised a young coon on the ground at the foot of the tree.

It may have been a venturesome youngster who had fallen from the tree and had not yet been retrieved by its mother. In any event, it could not climb back by itself, and after a few unsuccessful attempts, gave up. Racing to a young pine, the coon managed to clamber into its lower branches, and then began one of the funniest exhibitions the boy had ever seen.

There are few animals more at home in trees than full-grown raccoons, but most of this youngster's short life had been spent inside a deep hole. It had still to find its climbing legs, and when it started to walk out on a limb that

became very apparent. After two or three faltering steps the young coon lost its balance and, scrambling madly for a foothold, swung under the limb. For a few moments it hung there like a jungle sloth and then, clawing wildly, managed to pull its fat little body up and across the limb. It was a major effort to get upright from that position, but at last it was done. Slowly it took a few more faltering steps, then suddenly the whole thing happened all over again. It was the same act as the circus clown on the tightrope, but the boy thought it funnier with a black mask and ringed tail. He left the young acrobat where it was, knowing that its mother would come to the rescue as soon as he was out of sight.

The boy had no such faith in a mother skunk the evening he surprised her and her family. They met at the

edge of the wood, the skunks crossing the path in Indian file as the boy came through the opening in the wall. The mother hurriedly led her young into the darkening thickets, all but the last one. It stopped uncertainly and then, completely confused, shuffled toward the boy. He reached down and picked it up by the scruff of the neck. It was too young to know how to use its nauseous scent, and it nestled in his arm like a small kitten. Would its mother come back to find it? The boy was afraid not, and he could not leave this trusting creature to die of starvation. It became one of the summer's pets.

It was early fall when the boy took his skunk back to the wood to be released. It had been a wonderful pet, playful and gentle. Its scent sacs had not been removed. This is a dangerous operation, at best, and since the skunk was to be freed it could not be deprived of its only means of defense. All summer the boy had played with it and carried it about in his arms, and there had never been the slightest odor. He knew the chance he was taking, that a sudden fright such as a leaping dog could be disastrous, but all had gone well. Now he set the black and white animal down in the middle of the path. Regretfully he said goodbye and started home. He looked back and his pet was walking at his heels. He broke into a run and so did the skunk, but it had grown fat and lazy from a summer's feeding on rich table scraps and it soon stopped, accepting its fate. From now on it must earn its own living.

A week later the two met again. There was no mistaking the pattern of that broad white marking. The skunk stopped and looked up. Slowly the boy approached, holding out his hand and talking in a low voice. He came closer, twenty feet, fifteen feet, ten feet, as the animal watched uncertainly. Then it turned and ambled away, stopping once to look back. In a week's time his pet had returned to the wild as he had hoped, but the boy was pleased to see that he was not entirely forgotten. Not once had it started to raise its tail.

The boy had not wanted to break up the skunk family, but when the wood is full of young things accidents will happen. Another accident made him sorry for all the trouble he caused a red squirrel.

A head-high hole in a pine had been used for years by all manner of birds and animals, but one spring it seemed to have no tenants. At least in all his passings to and fro the boy had seen no evidence that it was occupied. One morning he stopped to investigate. He put his hand inside, but it was just too high for him to reach bottom. The next time he came in from the old carriage house he brought with him an apple box, substitute enough for a ladder. It rocked perilously, but he mounted it and again reached inside the hole. This time, as his hand went deeper, it touched on something soft and warm. With great care he lifted it out and discovered that he had a baby

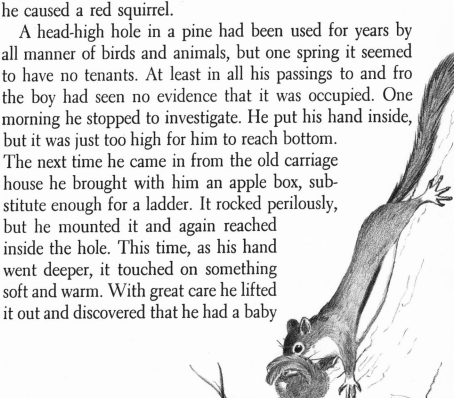

red squirrel. It looked at him from newly opened eyes that showed no fear, but he could feel its racing heart as the youngster tried to burrow inside his shirt. He thought for a moment what a lively pet it would make, but then he thought of the distraught mother. Regretfully, he put the squirming baby back in its nest.

When he came back from returning the box, the boy approached the big pine cautiously. He peeked through a low-hanging branch just in time to see the mother squirrel leaving her home. In her mouth, held gently by the loose skin of its belly, was one of her children. He could hear scratching sounds as she came down the rough bark, head first, and raced off across the pine needles. Her nest had been discovered, and she was moving her family to an emergency home. The boy left hurriedly; he had caused this family enough trouble. He hoped they would be safe and at least moderately comfortable in their new quarters.

There was one family in the wood who surprised the boy more than he surprised them. Years before, an epidemic of

mange had wiped out all the red foxes in this part of the country. Since he had been old enough to know the woods and fields at first hand, the boy had seldom seen a fox, but now they were coming back. At first they were scrawny and ragged, but at last a few healthy foxes had begun to appear. There was a fox den in the wood.

An old tree, toppled by a long-ago hurricane, had left its bare roots exposed to the weather. Under the tangle a fox had dug her burrow. The main entrance was plain to see, a spreading apron of packed dirt, and on it a few feathers and clean-picked bones. A smaller hole nearby was a back door.

It was on a morning when the boy had made a long and laborious approach through thick undergrowth that he saw the four cubs. They were playing at the mouth of their den, wrestling and tumbling over one another with baby snarls and barks. Their fur was a reddish-yellow, soft and woolly looking. The boy did not think that he had showed himself or moved, but suddenly they all dove below. Maybe the wind had carried his scent, or maybe the vixen, their mother, had seen him and warned them. In any event, they were gone.

The day was young and the boy wanted to see more of this family. He moved closer and settled himself comfortably in the low bush, no more than a dozen feet from the mouth of the den. The back entrance was also in view. When the pups reappeared, he would have a front row seat. Time went by: it seemed like hours. The heat of the day moved down to the floor of the wood, and all manner of insects discovered him. Had the young foxes

85

gone to sleep? Do they spend the day sleeping and come out again at dusk? He had no idea. To the boy these were unfamiliar animals.

It was no noise, no slightest sound, that finally made him turn slowly and look to his left. There, not ten feet away, was a reddish-yellow head with big ears and a sharp nose. Round eyes stared at him intently. The watcher was being watched. Through the low pine branches he saw a slight movement, the other cubs. There was a second back door he had not discovered! Then, as if by magic, they all disappeared.

Spring is the time when life is reborn. To the Indians it began with the Moon of the Young. Flowers push up from the roots of last year, insects appear after a winter of sleep, birds break out of their shells, and young animals open their eyes to the light of day. It is a time of excitement, a time of new life and hope. To the boy it is a time when the days are much too short and the nights too long.

# 9
# TREES OF THE WOOD

The First Trees of the Wood are, without question, its white pines. They stand in groves through whose high green roof thin shafts of sunlight slant down to the brown floor below. As they are the wood's most ancient trees, they are also its most numerous. The hardwoods may grow tougher wood, deeper roots, and stronger branches, but the white pines hold their own. They are rugged and vigorous, well able to compete with the new trees, and in this wood as in many others, to keep the upper hand.

In the early history of this country, white pines played an important role. When the British navy ruled the seas, tall, straight trees for masts were a necessity and, in Europe, very scarce. Parties of King's men roamed the forests of New England searching out such trees, some towering 200 feet and more into the skies. Many an unruly colonist was punished for cutting down a pine with the arrow mark of a "Crown Tree." White pines provided sturdy logs for the early settler's cabins, and when sawmills were built they became the most important wood for boards and timbers. Together with codfish and furs, pine lumber was one of the principal exports of early New England. Fortunes were made from the trade, and with this wealth the traders themselves used more pine to build the stately mansions that grace the elm-shaded streets of seaport cities.

Britain's supply of New England pine masts was cut off with the start of the Revolution. The majestic pine became a symbol of independence. Several of our first flags had white pines as emblems. When John Paul Jones set out to sail the seas a new flag, the Stars and Stripes, flew proudly from the top of his white pine mainmast. The big trees of the wood, the trees where crows, hawks, and owls nest, that have dropped their needles for long years to lay a soft, thick carpet at their feet, have a distinguished ancestry in the annals of this country.

There is only one other important conifer in the wood, the hemlocks. Where the brook winds through fern-covered boulders, hemlocks make a dense, damp shade where moss grows thick and deep. Most of the other trees of the wood are hardwoods; birches, beeches, oaks, maples, hickories, and the old sycamore. Their dead leaves build an acid soil through which a few plants, ferns, and grasses push their way, thin and fragile for the most part. And around the edge of the wood, along the stone walls and reaching out into fields and pastures, is a ring of low bushes and shrubs, cherries, shad, and poplar, with here and there a big elm that needs the full light of the sun to survive.

There are trees in the wood that are known to the boy by special names. The Old Sycamore or Coon Tree, the Horned Owl Pine, the Crow Tree, the Pileated Oak, and the Promethea's Cherries are all named for their inhabitants. Then there are the Leaning Hemlocks along the brook which start from the steep bank at an angle and then turn up, and the Holy Stub, a dead elm riddled with holes. There are other trees distinguished for some particular event or special feature, but the boy had found that such associations were not needed for interest. Trees are fascinating subjects by themselves, continually revealing new and unexpected secrets to those who search them out.

It was no easy task, at first, simply to recognize many of the trees of the wood at all seasons. With some, of course, it was no problem. The peeling white bark of a big canoe birch, the patchwork trunk of the sycamore, or the smooth gray bole of a beech is their identification at any time. In early spring there is no mistaking the scarlet blossoms of red maples, the white clouds of shadbushes, or the striking display of the dogwood by the old carriage house. When leaves unfold they mark beyond question the oaks, maples, and hickories, and fortunately, the poison ivy that clambers

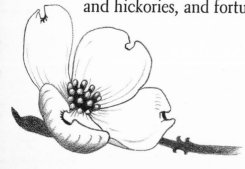

over stone walls in all too many places. And when a tree bears fruit, this is often the most certain identification of all. It seems hardly possible to mistake the dangling red cherries of a chokecherry, or an acorn, or the long pitchy cone of a white pine. But there are many different kinds of oaks and maples, and some trees and shrubs have no obvious features. During the winter months especially they present real problems.

When branches are stripped bare and fallen leaves hide beneath the snow, every tree and bush offers four telltale clues: its bark, twigs, buds, and leaf scars. Sometimes one of these alone is all that is needed; at other times, all four. As well as he knew the wood, the boy continually came across trees that were new to him or that he had forgotten, and he considered each one a challenge to his detective ability.

As a tree reaches upward, its bark does not grow up with it. Bark that was a foot above ground when the tree was very young is still a foot above ground when the tree has become a giant. It has not moved up, but it has been forced to expand constantly. Each year the tree has grown another layer of wood just under its bark, the familiar "tree rings" that can be counted to discover its age. And each new ring pushes the bark out that much more.

Most trees have bark that grows thicker with each passing year, with the dead outside layers splitting and cracking as the girth increases. The long, deep cracks of an old white pine or an oak are formed this way. A few trees shed their older layers. The base of a shagbark hickory is always surrounded with long strips of bark that have lost their

hold as they were pushed outward. The new bark of a sycamore is green at first, turning to white, then brown, and finally flaking off. White and yellow birches are constantly peeling, their thin outer skins hanging in paper curls until they are carried away by the winds. A very few trees such as beeches have bark that does not die but continues growing and expanding without either cracking or shedding. With the limited number of tree varieties in the wood, their bark is often all that is needed to recognize them. This is not true, however, of the shrubs and bushes, many of which look much alike. Nor is it true of young trees such as birches, whose bark is red with white markings, more like cherry than birch.

The relative importance of twigs, buds, and leaf-scars in recognizing trees varies. There are black willows along the brook where it flows through the marsh whose shiny yellow twigs are often the brightest part of a drab winter day. The twigs of sassafras are a clear green, and the small red-osier dogwoods have brilliant red twigs, a favorite food of deer, mice, and rabbits. But there are a few trees which can be identified surely by their twigs alone. Buds and leaf-scars are much more definite.

Buds do not suddenly appear in the spring. The leaves and flowers that unfold early in the season come from buds which were formed the year before, and as they expand tiny new buds appear, the leaves and flowers of a year to come. In autumn when leaves loose their grip and sail away before chilling winds, they leave scars on the twigs, and above those leaf-scars are the buds, ready to outlast the cold of winter. Those buds and leaf-scars, together, may

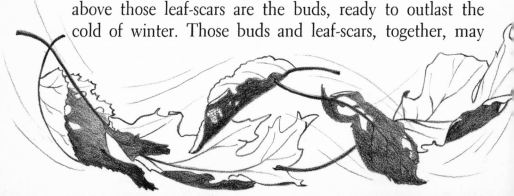

be the most important clues in winter.

The position of the buds on a twig is one of the first things to look for. On maples, ash, and some other trees they are opposite one another, but on most they are staggered. Then they may be large or small, have scales or just a single cap like pussy willows. Sometimes the bud at the tip of the twig is enough. The flower bud at the end of a flowering dogwood twig looks nothing like the leaf buds below it, but it can hardly be mistaken for anything else. It is held up on a short stalk and looks like a fat, silvery button topped with a peak. When the bud swells with spring sap, its four scales do not fall off but grow out like beautiful white petals, the original scales becoming the discolored spots on their notched edges. The dogwood flower is a small green cluster, almost unnoticed in the center of each spreading white cup.

When the boy began to notice leaf-scars, he opened up a whole new world of fantasy. Many of them are small and inconspicuous, but a hand lens shows a parade of weird and startling figures. Some scars are round, some triangular, and some are like crescent moons. The leaves that left them were connected to the twig by a number of tiny pipelines through which sap flowed, and these have left dots inside the scars. They are the features in faces that, in many cases, a cartoonist would envy.

Arriving at home after a winter's walk in the wood, the boy emptied his pockets of a collection of twigs. He spread them out under a strong light and examined them carefully with a hand lens. Here was a thin twig, bending a little at each pointed bud. The reddish-brown bud had sev-

Elm

eral scales with dark edges. It was tipped a bit above the leaf-scar, a triangle with rounded corners. The dots made eyes on a flattened dwarf face, and the bud was a tall hat tipped at a rakish angle. This was an elm twig.

Sumac

There were two that might have been circus clowns with balloon noses. One was the side bud and scar of a sumac twig; the other the terminal bud of a white ash. The ash bud was complete with ears and a velvety brown suede hat. There was a butternut twig dotted with pony heads for the clown parade, ponies wearing tall hats with furry brims and with a round jewel set in the front of

White Ash

each. And the pignut hickory scar was the clown who looks so sad that he is always the funniest of all. Not all leaf-scars or buds are as individual as these, but there are faces in the winter woods that, once recognized, are never forgotten.

It was a constant surprise to the boy that so few people think of trees as flowering plants, or even realize that giant pines and spreading oaks have blossoms just as surely as flowering dogwood, shad, and trees of the orchard. Because they do not advertise themselves they are often over-looked, not only by people but also by insects. If there

Butternut

were no bees to fertilize the blossoms of an apple orchard, there would be no apples, but pines would continue to thrive if all the insects in the world were suddenly eliminated.

In spring, clusters of male pollen-cones appear near the tips of a pine's upper branches. A big tree has thousands of such clusters, and each cone produces hundreds of thousands of pollen grains. When the cones open it needs only

Pignut
Hickory

a slight breeze to carry pollen into the air in yellow clouds.

96

The boy remembered well the consternation that occurred when a sudden shower fell through pollen-filled air. Yellow water collected in puddles and ran down windows and drain spouts. People everywhere were certain that a great catastrophe had taken place. It was the Day of the Yellow Rain.

In spite of the great waste, there is so much pine pollen in the air that enough filters down into the open scales of the fruiting cones to reach the waiting eggs, the future seeds. Other trees have developed ingenious ways to help disperse their pollen. The long catkins of poplar, willow, birch, hickory, and many others dangle in space where every breath of wind will shake loose puffs of yellow dust. Most trees and grasses, and many flowers throw their pollen lavishly into the air. Hay fever sufferers are well aware of that fact.

The first plants, the algae of long ago, were able to convert air and water into starch by means of chlorophyl, and plants have been doing it ever since. It is chlorophyl that colors plants green, and without it there would be no life on earth, either plant or animal. The leaves that clothe the bare limbs in spring combine the water piped to them from tree roots with the air they drink in to produce starch and sugar which they then feed back into the tree. Each leaf is a factory, and it is chlorophyl that makes the factories run.

The importance of leaves is overwhelming, but since the boy was no scientist his interest was in their more obvious features. The shape of a leaf is one of the first and often best means of identification. He wondered why

one tree, and only one, has leaves that are not identical. Sassafras has three leaves with different shapes. He never understood why tamaracks, which have needle-shaped leaves and cones like the cone-bearing evergreens, drops its needles just as the hardwoods do.

The boy marvelled at the changing and often brilliant colors of autumn when the leaves' pipelines dry up and their green chlorophyl dies, allowing their other colors to show through. His collection of autumn leaves, usually paraffined or sprayed with shellac or plastic, grew bigger every year. But there were so many other things in the wood that demanded his attention that he usually accepted leaves as they were and asked few questions of them.

The time between tree flower and fruit is usually the time between spring and fall. This is true of oaks, hickories, and other nut trees, of the orchard's fruit trees and many berry-bearing shrubs and trees. It is also true of ash, basswood, and most maples whose winged seeds fly before the winds of autumn. The sycamore even holds some of its seeds through the winter, dangling them in round balls from its bare twigs.

There are trees, however, that are in a hurry to get their flower and seed production over and done with. One such is the red maple. It is the first tree to bloom in the spring, bringing the marsh and the edge of the wood to sudden life in a blaze of scarlet. The blossoms are followed by leaves as brilliantly colored, but while they are still unfolding the winged seeds, dangling in clusters on slim stalks, are maturing. Before the leaves are fully grown the seeds have already fluttered away.

"By their fruits ye shall know them." Also by their leaves, bark, blossoms, buds, and leaf-scars. The creatures who live in the wood give it life and action, but the boy found pleasure of a different sort in learning to know its trees. They do not reveal their secrets to the casual observer, but they unlock them readily for a friend.

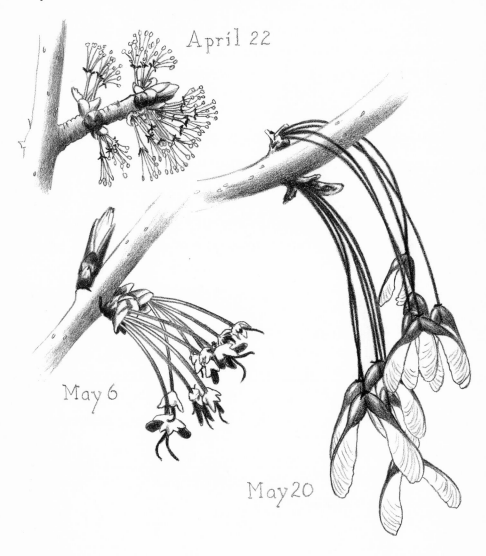

April 22

May 6

May 20

## IO

# UNEXPECTED MEETINGS

A movement under a tangle of bushes caught the boy's attention. Was it a cottontail? A bird quietly slipping onto its nest? He approached cautiously, kneeling down at last to peer into the deep shadows. Then he saw it, and almost fell over backward in surprise. Not three feet away an angry eye glared at him, a wild, fierce eye under a beetling brow. Then he made out a sharp, curved beak and realized it was a hawk. But why was a hawk skulking in such an unlikely place?

As the boy parted the long grass and pulled aside a screening branch, the bird suddenly threw itself on its back. Spread claws with needle-sharp talons that could drive deep into unprotected flesh reached up at him. It was a sharp-shinned hawk; and then the reason for its being

103

in such an unexpected spot became apparent. One wing spread out beside it at an odd angle. It was broken.

Sharp-shins are among the worst enemies of small birds. They are not soaring hawks but fly fast and low, swooping in and out of the edge of the wood, skimming over the tops of small trees and bushes, ready to swerve in a split second and dive on surprised birds below. The boy had seen them plunge headlong into thick tangles where small birds had fled for refuge. He had marvelled that they didn't break their wings at such speed. This one had. He looked at it with a mixture of pity and a feeling that this was a deserved fate, brought on by its own recklessness.

The boy went on his way, undecided whether, on his return, he should take the hawk with him and try to mend its broken wing, or mercifully put it out of the way. He was spared the decision. When he came back it had gone.

The wood is always interesting, but it is unexpected meetings such as this that make it exciting. The boy would long remember his excitement when he investigated a tangle of spider webbing under a boulder's overhang. As he swung the beam of his flashlight through the dark mass it picked out a hanging egg sac. It looked like a little brown paper bag, and beside it was a round, shiny black widow spider. He had barely time to see the two red spots on its underside before the surprised creature scuttled back down a funnel-shaped corridor into hiding.

Almost every kind of spider uses poison to kill its prey and to defend itself. Few of them, however, have venom which is strong enough to do more than raise a bee-sting swelling on humans. In this part of the world black widows are the one exception. Their bites are truly dangerous. They cause great pain and, in a very few cases, may result in death.

The boy knew the black widow's reputation, but he wondered how anyone could possibly get bitten. With a stick he tried to get her to come out in the open. She retreated as far back as she could go, making no attempt to defend herself, and when the webbing in the far corner was broken, down she fell to the ground as though dead, her eight legs doubled up under her body. The boy left her there, but he took the

egg sac with him. It would never let its hundreds of baby spiders loose in his wood.

Almost as surprising was the boy's first encounter with Thalessa, an ichneumon fly. He saw her first in flight with her long "tail" trailing behind like the streamer of an advertising plane. She lighted on a limb nearby, paying no attention to the watching boy as she proceeded to clean herself.

Ichneumon, "the tracker," is a fly that hunts down other insects on which to lay her eggs, and Thalessa is the

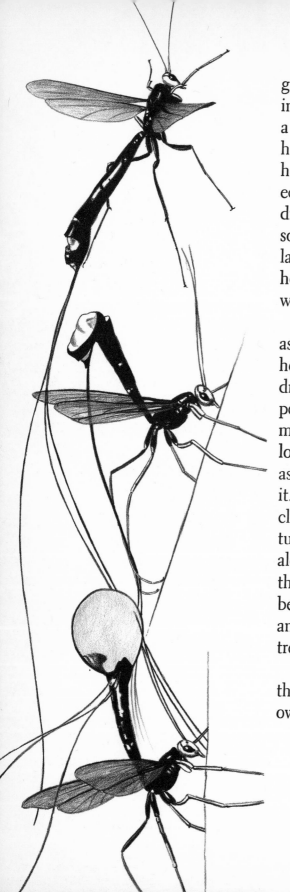

giant of her kind, almost two inches long. Her "tail" is really a drill, hardly bigger than a horsehair and three times as long as her body, protected by a pair of equally thin sheaths. With this drill she bores into solid wood, sometimes as deep as an inch, to lay her eggs in the tunnels of horntail grubs, food for her young when they hatch.

The boy watched in disbelief as that long drill, pulled through her hind legs for cleaning, was drawn up into her body, to reappear near its rear end inside a thin membrane. The transparent yellow circle grew bigger and bigger as more of the drill was added to it. When Thalessa had finished cleaning and her body had returned to normal, she took a few alert steps along the limb as though hunting for signs of life below, then rose like a helicopter and disappeared through the trees.

Insects are not as plentiful in the wood as in the pond or meadow, though there are times during the mosquito season when the boy would argue the point. Tree living, however, has developed some insects with shapes and habits that are unique. The boy would never forget his first sight of the twig that walked away.

It was on a day in late summer. Not a breath of air stirred and leaves hung motionless. Buds were well developed, ready for the long, cold months ahead. The boy was examining them with his hand lens, making notes against the day when there would no longer be leaves to help him name the trees of the wood. Then, as he was about to shift his attention to a new twig, it moved. He lowered his glass in astonishment. The leaf-green "twig" had long, spindly legs and hair-like antennae. It was a walking stick, an insect whose camouflage is so perfect that it escapes the attention of many a bird who would like to make a meal of it.

There are other insects who imitate twigs, leaves, and even flowers. Caterpillars of a large

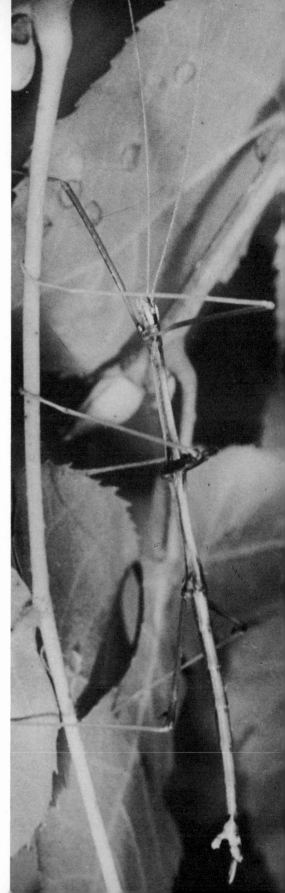

family of small moths, the Geometrids, are among the world's best mimics. Here and there along the gray twigs of a hickory tree, short dead stubs stand out stiffly. The boy moved about under the low branches, touching each stub in turn. Unlike his experience with the walking stick, this time he knew exactly what he was looking for, and at last he was successful. One was not hard and stiff, but bent at his touch. There was another giveaway, a short length of silk that tied its tip to the hickory twig. The boy nudged it with his finger and the "dead twig" came to life. Its camouflage had been penetrated, and as it looped away it looked like only one thing, a mottled gray inchworm, just what it was.

There is nothing unusual about finding plant galls. They are everywhere, strange growths on trees, plants, and shrubs. The unusual thing about galls is that no one has yet been able to explain them fully. It is known that most of them are caused by insects who lay their eggs in plant tissues.

When the eggs hatch, the plants form peculiar growths around the larvae. What is not known is why they always form the same growths around the same kind of larvae.

There are probably more different varieties of galls on oaks than on any other tree or plant, more than three hundred. They are caused by the larvae of flies, wasps, midges, mites, and other creatures. Some of these larvae are so much alike that it is almost impossible to tell them apart, yet the tree builds exactly the right shelter for each one. Here it lives and eats in privacy or with others of its kind, until it becomes an adult and works its way out.

One kind of oak apple, as big as a ping-pong ball, has a tiny larval wasp in a cell at its center, held to the shell by radiating threads. The tree concentrates food in the gall, and the insect feeds without ever moving from its safe retreat.

There are oak galls that look like pink and white balls of wool, small chestnut burrs, acorns, buttons, and spiked war clubs. Willows have "pine cone" galls, hickories produce galls that are small copies of their own nuts, and the stalks of goldenrod are often interrupted by round swellings. Almost 1,500 gall-making creatures have been iden-

tified in this country, and few plants are immune from their attentions. The boy's gall collection added nothing to scientific knowledge, but when their inhabitants emerged he knew the makers, at least. He would leave the unravelling of the riddles they posed to others.

Among the riddles is how some of the gall-makers have developed the unusual ability of producing generations that are nothing like the original insects. They go to different kinds of trees and produce completely different galls. Several generations may go by before the cycle is complete and they return to their original forms and habits. It makes things very confusing to the scientists who are trying to classify them.

As he walked through the wood one morning, the boy was startled when a screech owl suddenly burst from cover and flew directly across his path. At this time of day the owls of the wood should be sound asleep, resting after a busy night of hunting. Further, since screech owls live in nest holes, this bird should not have been in the open whether awake or asleep. The boy was puzzled, but the answer came sooner than he expected.

Just ahead was a big maple. For years it had raised a dead stub on high, and in that stub was a screech owl's hole. At dusk the boy had often seen a sleepy-looking bird at the round opening. Now disaster had struck. The stub lay on the ground, broken in several pieces, and the owl's home had split wide open. Had there been young birds in the nest? It was May, the right time of year. Suspicious, the boy retraced his steps, and when the owl appeared again, snapping its beak as it flew close to his head, he knew there were, indeed, young nearby.

The bird had come from a thick stand of young pines, so it was there the boy began his hunt. Parting the green cover, he peered into tree after tree, and before long his search was rewarded. There, pressed close against the slim

trunk, were two sleepy, fuzzy young owls. They gazed at him mournfully, eyelids drooping now and then as though they could hardly stay awake. For long minutes they stared at one another, until the boy began to feel sleepy himself. Such is the power of suggestion.

There are places in the wood where the boy can always expect the unexpected. Rotted logs and loose stones are hiding places for all manner of things, especially if the ground beneath them is damp. Almost every old log has its complement of beetles, grubs, sow bugs, wood roaches, and millipedes, and turning over a stone can be a real adventure. Sometimes a little red newt or a salamander looks up in surprise at the unexpected daylight, then wriggles hurriedly into hiding again. Every now and then a slim red-bellied or ring-necked snake is uncovered, wrapped in a tight coil. A colony of termites, their tunnels thrown wide open, scurry about in confusion while ants rush in to pounce on them and carry them away.

It was under the overhang of a moss-covered log that the boy came on a red-backed salamander curled around her eggs. Unlike most of her relatives, who lay their eggs in water and then forget them, she had hung hers like a bunch of grapes in this damp, protected spot, and she was standing guard until they hatched. It was a rare find.

Except for birds like the inquisitive chickadees or the loud crows and jays, most of the creatures of the wood are quiet and furtive. They spend the day in hiding and when night falls the wood comes alive with their rustlings and whisperings. On occasion the boy slept out under the trees. He could recognize the squeak of a mouse, the bark

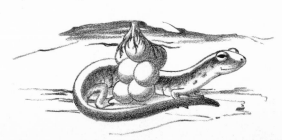

of a fox, or the hooting of an owl, but most of the sounds of night left him with questions unanswered.

At times the boy wondered what held the greatest pleasure and interest for him in the wood. Was it the mysteries of night, the unexpected meetings of day, the towering trees or the flowers that hid at their feet? He knew well it was a combination of these and much more.

As he clambered over the barway into the pasture, a flock of chickadees followed the boy to the very edge of the wood. Their cheery chattering bade him godspeed. He waved back, knowing that these wood sprites would watch over things and report to him on his return. If he could not understand their reports, he could be sure they would be complete, for nothing escapes their attention. As the pines are the First Trees of the Wood, so are the chickadees its First Citizens.

# INDEX

# Index of Drawings and Photographs

# ABOUT THE AUTHOR

For twenty-five years Henry B. Kane has been writing and illustrating outdoor books. His well-remembered Wild World Tales, a series of life histories of animals, made a notable contribution to children's nature literature. Now, in THE TALE OF A WOOD, he continues the fascinating and exciting story of plants and animals in relation to their surroundings so well begun in THE TALE OF A MEADOW and THE TALE OF A POND.

Born in Cambridge, Massachusetts, Mr. Kane was educated at Exeter and the Massachusetts Institute of Technology. A one-time Naval Aviator, his business career has been in engineering, sales, and advertising. For the past two decades he has been director of the M. I. T. Alumni Fund.

With his wife and daughter, Electa, Mr. Kane lives in Lincoln, Massachusetts, a town near Boston which still retains enough wildness to provide plentiful material for his discerning pen and camera.